The Machine of Ultimate Prizes

for Helen,
my talented & artistic
big sister!
With lots of love.
Rose
x

The Machine of Ultimate Prizes

by Rose Cleaver-Emons

Practical Inspiration Publishing
2014

First published in Great Britain 2014 by Practical Inspiration Publishing

© Rose Cleaver-Emons 2014

The moral rights of the author have been asserted.

ISBN (print): 978-1-910056-12-7
ISBN (ebook): 978-1-910056-13-4

Table of Contents

Dedication

For Grandpa Bert, whose charm, grace and entrepreneurial spirit continue to inspire me.

About the Author

Rose arrived in the world Norwich in 1975, shortly before moving to Nigeria, which she doesn't remember. Daughter of a disillusioned Chartered Accountant (who later was inspired to become a vicar) and a musical mother (who frequently played piano and violin and created the best paddling pool parties ever), she moved house and schools a lot in the early years, wore hand-me-down clothes and soon became a Goth.

After learning to play saxophone and piano, sing, climb trees, build dens, ride motorbikes, joining her first rock band (surprisingly she was not offered a record deal), and writing plays which were mainly performed in the playground, Rose left the Isle of Wight and went to Goldsmiths University in London for a culture shock and to discover life.

She did this with great gusto for three years, discovering a fantastic Goth scene and numerous music festivals, which is probably why she only got a 2:2 in her first degree.

She then went on to do a PGCE and an MA in Theatre and Directing, created or joined several more bands, theatre groups and a Gospel choir (this time somewhat more successfully) and worked directing and teaching theatre.

Rose's final Goth band took her to California, the home of the man she was in love with. Later that year he committed suicide. This taught Rose to value time, people and above all to celebrate every moment that is, rather than mourning the moments that aren't.

Rose moved back to London, taking a job at The Coopers Company & Coborn school of Upminster, and of course, joining another Goth band and touring—this time in the school holidays! She continued to direct, forming the U4ria Theatre company through which much fun was had and several performers inspired, many of whom still professionally perform and direct in the theatre world.

Rose also discovered that extreme sports were just as much fun as motorbikes and added this to her collection of life.

After a few years, Rose found herself training and mentoring teachers, negotiating for the Unions, and being lent out to other schools across the county in addition to teaching the A-level and GCSE students part time.

And the rock band. And the theatre company. And the extreme sports.

After a few years, she became a little bored with the less hands-on aspects of the job and asked the headmaster in a cheeky and rather direct way if she could have one day a week to set up projects to raise the school's profile locally through Theatre and Training. To Rose's utter shock, not only did the Headmaster agree, he even contributed towards her first NLP training course.

From here, Rose spent more time in the community and less time in the classroom. She studied Practitioner, then Master Practitioner and finally Trainer Level NLP, Hypnosis, Timeline Therapy™ and Coaching and set up her own communication and training company combining the creativity and story of theatre with the empowerment of Timeline Therapy™, the meditation of Hypnosis and the communication skills of NLP.

On May 1st 2009, Rose went on a hang-gliding blind date to Upminster Airfield where she met the wonderful Michael. A year later, the future in-laws were introduced to one another at the foot of Europe's highest bungee jump as Rose and Michael did a death-defying leap for charity. On December 19th 2010, on a crisp snowy day in Essex, they were married in a medieval priory. And there was much rejoicing.

Summer 2011 after discovering she was pregnant, Rose decided it was time to leave the world of PAYE forever and Life Returns (and 9 months later Joseph) were born.

Rose currently works as a Trainer of NLP, Hypnotherapy and Timeline Therapy (r) and a Master coach, as well as running the Northwest Vibrant Networking region and working as an Independent Consultant with Arbonne.

And of course being full-time Mummy to a lively two and a half year old.

And writing books.

And...

Acknowledgments

To my publisher Alison Jones—thank you so much for pulling out all the stops to turn this around in record time! To Ian Prowse for encouraging and supporting me in many ventures—thank you for who you are and for being such an example of the ability to combine a genuine love for people with a passion for great business. To the Bromsgrove Mastermind gang—Vicky, Ethan, Les, Bill- thank you for kicking me up the backside to get on with creating the first in the series!

Thank you Catt and David, Laura and Cat for making the Northwest an even friendlier place when I first arrived! Thank you to the whole of Vibrant—especially the Northwest Vibrant crew—you are totally amazing people and I consider you friends as well as great business builders. Thank you James French for being an inspiring living example of how leadership can be as well as an encourager and true creative!

To my Mum, Dad and sister—thank you for your love and all I have learned from you. To all the family and especially Rob and Jude—thank you for all the family gatherings at the farm and for being there to chat to over the years—and inspiring me in business. To my grandparents—You were all amazing, loving wonderful people who led lives of travel, creativity, learning and love. I am so blessed that I got to enjoy your company over so many years. I think of you often.

To my dearest friends—Chrissie, Frances, Esther, Alex and Kat, Jase and Mim, Matt, and all the many wonderful goths and musicians past and present that have helped me along the way. I consider myself truly blessed to know and love friends with such integrity. Thank you JT for teaching me the lesson of the butterfly. Thank you David Shepard, Alistair and Claire Hegarty for reminding me that life is magical.

And finally, most importantly of all the biggest thank you of all to Michael for being the most loving, kind, generous, thoughtful and supportive husband a girl could wish for, and a fantastic daddy to Joseph.

And to Joseph.

You are the bringer of joy.

I am who I am because of all of you.

With Love.

Rose

Foreword

When Rose asked me to write the foreword for her new book *The Machine of Ultimate Prizes* I was over the moon. Having read the manuscript a few weeks previously and being totally blown away by it, it was a really easy decision. There are so many business and life lessons within the pages of this book and if you recognise them and use them within your everyday life they are sure to have a hugely positive impact.

Rose is a lady who very much practises what she preaches, she is my regional director for the North West with Vibrant Network and uses the principles in *The Machine of Ultimate Prizes* to ensure that she is consistently one of the top performers in our fast-growing network as well as in her own Personal Development Business as a certified trainer in NLP, Hypnosis, Timeline TherapyR and as a Master Coach working with private clients and delivering training.

When Rose started her journey with Vibrant Network she had just moved to the North West of England, had no contacts or family within the area and was totally starting from scratch. Three weeks from the date Rose moved house, she had successfully launched the first of her Vibrant groups.

Vibrant Network is a Personal Development and Business Networking organisation that is very much based on building emotional connections, developing business relationships and group learning. I know from personal experience how hard it can be to create an engaged network in a new area—especially with a group like Vibrant Network that is very different to the norm. It is a huge testimony to Rose that she has managed to launch multiple successful groups in the North West from a standing start and has built a strong team of leaders in the area, each of whom now run multiple groups of their own. She frequently speaks at Vibrant events and loves sharing her skills to assist others.

Rose is a real inspiration to not only me, but to all of her colleagues and friends within the Vibrant Network and beyond. One thing that I have come to realise with Rose is that when she commits to something—you can consider it done. This book is a great example of Rose and her commitment to taking action regardless of how 'realistic' the outcome is or how busy she already is.

Rose told me she was going to write a book and then a month later it was done! She runs a couple of businesses, her husband works away regularly with the BBC and she looks after her adorable 2-and-a-half-year-old son. But somehow she still managed to find the time to write this amazing book by getting up at 3am and working in the only quiet time available to get it done.

If you take time to study this book and the lessons throughout you too will be on a journey that you may have previously not thought possible.

Ian Prowse
Vibrant Network

Introduction

If you are reading this, you are very likely to be an entrepreneur, an independent thinker, or at the very least to know someone who is. Some people are born this way and begin their first independent ventures as soon as they can walk and talk. Others are 'born' accidentally and still others just decide their time has come. However you got here, well done for having the gumption to go for it. It's a lot easier to sit there complaining, but for those who decide to shape their own future, the ultimate prize awaits.

The Box of Dreams...

The truth is, we all start out with a box of dreams. Think of the four-year-old running around saying "I'm going to be an astronaut", or "I can fly". For some strange reason, as we grow, we are surrounded by opinions. And it can take a little while to realise that when someone says, "You can't do that—it'll never work", it's because for them, in their model of the world, it would be impossible.

But that's just it.

That's THEIR model of the world.

Not yours.

And no matter how much you love them, it's OK to think differently.

It's time to open the Box of Dreams...

This is a story about you, and me... and, well... a lot of people around here. Only you know whether you are more of

a Jenny, a Jack or a Joe... and ultimately only you can choose how you read this book.

You might read it as a fun story, laugh and then continue as you were. Or you may decide to use some of the secrets contained in these pages to transform your chances of success. Just one simple idea really can be the difference that makes the difference.

However you choose to enjoy this book is just fine. It's for you. It's a gift. Enjoy.

The Author

The Machine of Ultimate Prizes

Once upon a time, there was a fairground. The fairground was a magical place—people bought and sold sparkles, luck, treasures and rides. Some people spent time on the rides, hoping for as much fun as possible; others sought out the fortune tellers, hoping to be told some amazing thing that would change their lives—or at least let them know what to expect next; still others played on the machines, hoping to win prizes.

Everyone hoped they might win something.

Of course there were also those who worked for the ringmaster and kept everything at the fairground running smoothly.

At the centre of the fairground was an ancient and powerful machine. Above it hung a sign: 'The Machine of Ultimate Prizes'.

More about this later.

Three of the people whose families worked in the fairground were called Jack, Jenny and Joe. As children, they had been told about some of the things the fairground had to offer—things they might enjoy (or not) when they were 'just a little bit bigger', whatever that meant.

Jack's parents had told him all about the rides.

"Be careful," they had said, "they go down as well as up. And remember what goes up must come down! It always does. It always has been and always will be. So be careful."

Jenny knew about the machines as her father oiled them daily and her mother polished them.

"By all means work with the machines," said her mother. "Just don't ever expect to get anything out of them. For a start, people like us never do, and secondly," she added "you'll only ever win a little prize each time and you should be grateful as it's more than you deserve"

And for a while, Jenny was happy with her lot.

Joe's parents worked with the buses. "The fairground will always need buses," said Joe's father. "Your grandfather and his father before him were all drivers on the buses. People can't get from the station to the fairground without us."

So Joe had grown up to become a bus driver. His mum had been ever so proud when he got his first uniform.

He'd looked just like his dad.

Now, as we mentioned, right at the centre of the fairground was the 'Machine of Ultimate Prizes'. It was the machine that kept, sustained and ran the fairground smoothly. Its prizes looked after the workers busying about the fairground.

All under the watchful gaze of the Ringmaster.

It was a curious machine, with many different colours and lights and a special slot to put a penny in and a big lever.

The curious thing was that to win a small prize, all you had to do was ask the Ringmaster each month on the same day to pull the lever. And as long as you were working on the fairground, as sure as eggs is eggs and as regular as clockwork out would pop your little prize.

If you were to put a penny in the slot, you might get a little prize out, you even had a chance of winning a bigger prize. However, only a few people ever put pennies into the machine—it was far too risky.

The Machine of Ultimate Prizes

Most 'sensible' people waited for the ringmaster to pull the lever. There was a reason for this. If you put a penny into the machine, you *might* win a prize. If you did, there would be a whirring sound and the lever would move by itself, dispensing a small (sometimes even medium and very occasionally large) prize out.

IF you won.

And you might not.

If you didn't, the machine would make a loud embarrassing belching sound and unceremoniously spit your coin out onto the pavement in full view of everyone around.

Right at the top of the machine, on top of all the prizes, was a small box made of pure gold. A little tag read: 'The Box of Dreams'.

This was the ULTIMATE prize.

The one everyone dreamed of winning.

Many stories had been written about the Ultimate Prize. Songs were sung and films were made. The older generation had seen it all before. They warned against the dangers of the Box of Dreams and extolled the virtue of being 'content with your lot'.

Some said the Box of Dreams was empty—just a gimmick to get people to put their coins into the Machine of Ultimate Prizes. Others said it had already been won and therefore they didn't believe they could ever win or that anyone else could.

Others would tell of all the folks they had seen pouring their shiny pennies into the machine only to receive loud belch after loud belch by way of response.

"And my goodness what it did to their poor families!" they would say, shaking their heads sadly.

But every now and again,
  along came someone
      who refused to listen to the opinions
          and decided to give it a go.

Jack, Jenny and Joe had all been raised on the fairground and their parents had taught them to accept that if they were one of the 'lucky ones' working at the fairground, once a month the ringmaster would pull the lever and dispense them a small prize in exchange for all their hard work.

And that is how life works.

It is 'correct' and 'as it should be'.

And although it's OK to moan every now and again, things really are better off as they are.

Sure enough, once a month, an identical small prize would be dispensed and off they would go, working on the fairground, until the next month when it would happen again exactly the same way.

OK, so it was predictable, even a little boring at times, but it was safe: they knew what they were getting and they were sure to get it.

Well, the years went by and Jack, Jenny and Joe grew up. Jack worked with the tickets, Jenny with the machines creating warning labels for them, and Joe drove the buses.

Just like their parents before them.

Until one day, something changed...

Joe's Story

Joe was a small man, with a twinkle in his eye and a dream in his heart. For many years, Joe had worked on the buses.

And as he drove people from A to B, or B to A (sometimes even via X when he was called to do so), Joe often found his head was filled with ideas.

Some of them were fun ideas, some could make him rich and some might help others. He dreamed of winning a lottery ticket and buying a big prize, but so often the dog ate his ticket and on the occasions when it didn't, his numbers never quite added up.

He thought perhaps he would invent something and it would make him famous. There was a popular show on TV called 'The Hornet's Nest' or something like that, in which famous wealthy investors would watch impoverished inventors showing their latest ideas.

Sometimes they were laughed at and left empty handed, but other times the 'hornets' got really excited and very, very occasionally someone would invent something amazing like a new flavour of burger relish and the investors would make them millionaires.

That's what the world needs, thought Joe. A new flavour of burger relish, what a helpful invention.

But it had already been done.

The day 'IT' happened began just like any other.

Joe had collected his bus, Sally, from the stand. She was a lovely dark green bus with a white stripe on the side and a

COME IN!

big sign saying 'Chips For Tea—Happy Days!' in foot-high letters on the side, with a big picture of a surprisingly slim family eating chips and smiling.

He had casually sauntered over, spinning the keys in his hand and whistling. The keys span off his finger and dropped in a puddle. As he bent down to pick them up, he came face to boot with the large feet of 'Lurch', the tall gangly manager. Lurch wasn't smiling.

"Things have changed round here," said Lurch. "People like to drive cars these days. The bus depot is being flattened to make way for a carpark. Only one bus will be running as a tourist attraction and I'll be driving that. Everyone else… well… we'll have to let you go."

To his credit, he did look rather forlorn about the whole thing.

So that was it.

One fairly nondescript five minutes later and the Ringmaster pulled the lever for Joe for the last time. "That's it," he said. "You'll have to find your own prizes now."

Three small prizes were handed to Joe in a paper bag.

"Well it can't be that hard can it?" he thought to himself.

Joe had always been a positive person. "I'm just an Average Joe and if I can do it, anyone can! I'll just have to go out there and find some shiny pennies and hope that they're the right ones to earn me prizes."

He looked up at the machine.

"One day I'd love to win the Ultimate Prize," he thought, "but for now, any prize would be nice."

And 'Joe the bus driver' became 'Joe the Entrepreneur'.

Jenny's Story

In one of the larger houses, over the other side of the fairground, a young genius called Jenny was finishing her coffee.

She smiled to herself. It was time for a change anyway, and she was glad it had happened the way it had. That way she could always say she had 'decided to move on'.

What had actually happened was this. Jenny had been to university. She had enjoyed studying for her degree. She wasn't a whizz kid, or a rich kid, a rebel or a cool kid or a weirdo (thank goodness).

Not like those strange people that used too much hairspray, turned up late for lectures because they'd been dancing the night away at the Slimelight club the night before, wore black and listened to too much Morrissey and The Cure[1]. She was very glad indeed that she wasn't one of those!

Jenny had sort of blended in at university. She always had. She attended the required amount of lectures and at least skim-read the first and last pages of all the books on the recommended reading list. She had a good circle of friends and partied a couple of times a week. She drank a reasonable amount and only threw up on her room-mate's biology paper just that one time.

She gained a 2:1 (just!) and sort of fell into her job making the warning stickers to stick on the machines at the fairground.

---

[1] *Note from the author: this is possibly why I got a 2:2 at university. But boy was it fun.

'This Machine is Alarmed'

'No Leaning' and one of her better ones:

'No One Under this Height or with Improper Facial Hair is Allowed on the Ghost Train for Health and Safety Reasons'

It always worked when you put 'for health and safety reasons' underneath whatever command you wanted the people to adhere to. She didn't know why, but for some reason no one ever questioned the logic, so whenever she could, Jenny would put 'for health and safety reasons' at the bottom of the label.

The truth was, she just didn't like moustaches.

It wasn't really the job she had wanted, but then, she hadn't really known what she'd wanted. It was a steady job, with a reliable salary and the prospect of getting a medium prize each month if she worked hard. Sometimes she even got flowers at Christmas.

So she stayed there, getting on with some people, avoiding others, gossiping about others, liking some bits of the job but not others, watching the clock from about 3pm, and generally getting on with it.

She made manager after five years, by steadily working her way up and being reliable. But deep down she felt she didn't quite 'fit'. She couldn't put her finger on what it was. It just wasn't 'quite' what she had hoped her life would turn out like when she was a little girl.

She wanted more.

And even though she had put the idea of winning the Box of Dreams into the smallest, furthest and darkest corner of her mind, every now and then she would remember it.

To tell the truth, she was a bit bored. She felt 'they' sometimes took advantage, what with all the meetings (they

LOVED meetings!), the unpaid overtime and the additional responsibilities. After a while she began to notice more and more of those little 'extra tasks' creeping in: 'because you're so good at it Jenny', 'only you know how to do this type of label', 'we trust you with this one', 'can we say the price of popcorn is for health and safety reasons?'

On and on it went. She hadn't been offered a raise in a few years now and was beginning to feel rather under-appreciated.

And then it was time.

It was a fairly average Friday night and Benjy's band were playing at the 'Slap 'n Tickle' pub on the high street. To be honest, they were pretty average as well. But it was there she happened upon Eddie.

Eddie was reasonably handsome in the dimly lit bar and looked almost smart compared to the sticky carpet the pub hadn't replaced in the last fifty years. He certainly talked a good game too.

Two years later they were married, on a rainy day in April. Sixteen years, three children and numerous disagreements later, they were divorced.

She should have known better than to marry a man with a moustache.

"It's time for a change," thought Jenny.

So after 18 years as manager, working in a small shared office in a corner of the Instructive Sticker Company, she decided to go in search of the shiny penny.

Not just any shiny penny.

The one that would release the top prize in the Machine of Ultimate Prizes: the Box of Dreams.

Jack's story

Jack had had several jobs. It wasn't so much that he didn't know what he wanted to do, it was more that he didn't like working for people if he felt he could do it better than them. And when they made rubbish decisions it made his blood boil.

He wasn't a difficult chap. He liked people and was OK with working. He could just see that there were better ways to do things and thought the bosses were a bit out of touch with the workers. When he told his bosses his ideas, they thanked him, and then reminded him of the value of 'thinking inside the box then making the box smaller' and 'grey-sky-with-a-chance-of-rain thinking', and sent him back to his desk.

Jack had never liked being told what to do. It irritated him; he already knew what to do and was perfectly OK with getting on with it uninterrupted.

He had tried 'thinking inside the box' and adopting the 'more-grey-sky-thinking' approach and various other initiatives his superiors brought in. Nothing really changed anyway.

With each new 'innovation', Jack would think to himself: "What's being presented here is nothing more than an old idea in a new box. Someone has just put a fancy name on something people have been doing for years and sold it to other people and made lots of money.

"So then the bosses buy it and spend time and money training me to do what I was already doing, just under a fancy heading, whilst somebody somewhere gets rich. And that somebody isn't me!"

Really though, if he was honest, the reason he didn't like that is because he wished he'd done it himself. If only HE could create a system and teach it to others instead of being on the receiving end. Of course he COULD do exactly that—all he needed to do was to step outside his comfort zone and do it.

But it was easier to moan than to take action.

And then one day, Jack had had enough.

He packed his desk, handed in his notice and left.

It was time to be his own boss.

He felt excited: this was, in his heart, what he'd always wanted—he just wished he'd done it sooner.

And so, three new entrepreneurs were born, each in search of the shiny penny that would win them the Ultimate Prize… that small, elusive gold box… the Box of Dreams.

What the Entrepreneurs Did Next

To begin with, Jack, Jenny and Joe did things in a similar way.

Here is (roughly and in no particular order) what they did:

1. Make a list of things I've always wanted to do.
2. Make a list of what I'm good at.
3. Tidy off my desk and make some kind of office space in the spare bedroom.
4. Think of a fancy name for my company.
5. Make the company official and register it.
6. Think of a name for the company that I like better.
7. Wish I'd registered that one instead, OR—re-register a new company.
8. Join a membership organisation so I feel like a 'proper' entrepreneur.
9. Open a company bank account so that I feel official.
10. Do a course of some kind. Get inspired.
11. Tidy the desk again…

And then it was time to search for the shiny penny that would lead to the Ultimate Prize: the Box of Dreams…

What Jack did Next

Jack was the first to find a shiny penny. He'd just been sitting in a coffee shop. He looked down and there it was, right in front of him! He was SO excited, he immediately called his friends to tell them all about it.

Next he spent time and money designing a very shiny website to tell the world about the shiny penny he had found, certain that if he put something on the internet about just how shiny his penny was, people would come flocking in.

It's a pity that Jack didn't look at other people's websites at this point as if he had, he would have discovered a lot of even shinier pennies than his out there on even shinier sites!

And then a curious thing happened.

Whilst Jack was still building his Very Shiny Website, he came across more shiny pennies!

He was amazed!

He was certain he could gather lots of really great prizes now as he had a collection of shiny pennies and not just the one. Jack rushed about picking up shiny pennies here there and everywhere, certain that one would lead him to the Ultimate Prize.

The only problem for Jack was that the discovery of all these newer shinier pennies made his first shiny penny look a bit dull. So he decided to take down the website, even though it had brought him one small prize, in order to develop a new one, to incorporate all his newer, shinier pennies.

He redesigned a newer, shinier website in the light of the new pennies he had found. He added pages and pictures, he tweeted and twittered, he told the world and used all the right social media channels. The only thing was, he was so pleased with all the shiny pennies he had found that he was trying to tell the world about ALL of them at once!

Which was a bit confusing for the people reading about them.

And made it even harder for them to find the website in the first place.

And as for Jack, he now had no idea which penny to put in the Machine of Ultimate Prizes.

Every time he got excited about his pennies, he would pull a great handful out of his pockets and walk along looking at them to try and decide which one he liked best. Some days he liked one best, some days another and other days he liked all of them.

But he never could find just one penny to put into the Machine of Ultimate Prizes. I mean, what if he lost it? Worse still, what if the machine spat it out again and made that embarrassingly loud belching sound?

The thought made him cringe.

No, he thought. I have a whole handful of valuable pennies. I'll just keep carrying them around and hopefully my luck will change.

One day, as Jack was walking along, examining a handful of pennies (and adding in a few new ones he'd found), he suddenly hit the wall.

Literally.

Right in the face.

It was very sore and he wished he had been looking at the path ahead instead of down at his pile of shiny pennies.

He looked up to see the Machine of Ultimate Prizes before him. He had no idea what to do with his pennies as he had gathered so many that they were weighing him down.

Overwhelmed, he started throwing pennies at the machine (ignoring the polite sticker which read 'Only One Penny at a Time Please, for Health and Safety Reasons'), shouting "Give me a prize! Give me a prize!"

He began to pick up the fallen pennies and throw them again and again in handfuls at the machine, hoping that by some random chance one would fall into the slot and the machine would dispense him the Ultimate Prize, the Box of Dreams.

To be honest, ANY prize would be good at this point.

As the pennies landed at Jack's feet there seemed to be more and more of them. In frustration he continued to throw great handfuls, not even looking at what he was throwing any more.

Even a medium prize would be nice, he thought. You know what? Actually I'd settle for a small prize.

This is so much harder than I thought it would be and I still have no idea what to do with all these shiny pennies.

Had he paused to look at what was in his hand, Jack would have realised that alongside the pennies he was also throwing lots of ring-pulls from soda cans without even noticing.

Jack continued this way for some time and then eventually looked down at his feet. He was so despondent by this time that all he could see were the ring pulls, scattered about his feet.

He had nothing left and no idea where the next little prize would come from.

Suddenly the safe 'little prizes' seemed bigger and more comforting than they ever had.

Shaking his head sadly, Jack went to see the Ringmaster to ask whether he had any jobs going, so that at least he could have that certainty back of knowing where the next little prize was coming from.

Jack was lucky enough to get a job cleaning the fairground rides, just like his dad had.

"Careful," he'd say to passers by, "They go down as well as up!"

But every night, in that quiet moment just before sleep, Jack would lie there and wonder to himself...

....What If?

What Jenny Did Next

Jenny took a different approach.

She decided that to get the bigger prizes (especially if she was to win the Ultimate Prize: the Box of Dreams), she needed to learn.

She knew she hadn't really applied herself in uni so she would make up for it now.

First of all, she taught herself book-keeping—every business needs a good book-keeper, she reasoned, and rather than use up the small prizes I've saved paying someone, I can do it myself.

And I will really care about the way it is done because I will be doing it for me.

Once she had qualified as a book-keeper, Jenny realised that every good business needs filing, admin and organising to be done well.

And who better than Jenny herself to do that? She already had the skills and even if it would take her a bit longer than having a professional PA, she would care so much more about how it was done.

She would ALWAYS do it right.

So Jenny learned how to be a PA.

Next she learnt how to create a website, to edit it, to use online advertising, to market, to make beautiful leaflets, to print those leaflets herself professionally, to design lovely letter-headed paper and to really make everything look nice.

It all took up quite a bit of Jenny's time.

After three years, Jenny had used up her small stash of saved-up prize but STILL hadn't put even one shiny penny into the Machine of Ultimate Prizes.

The pennies she had found had sat there on the shelf for so long now that they were actually looking a lot duller than they used to.

But Jenny didn't even have time to polish them.

She was too busy being her own PA, book-keeper, secretary, telephonist, advertiser and printer.

"Never mind," she said. "I have learnt a lot about how to do all the jobs my business needs and I will never need to pay anyone for anything as I can do absolutely everything myself."

And she went back to her desk.

She added up her expenses from the last three years, totalled her outgoings, cross referenced that with her penny storage jar, created a spreadsheet with all the things she had done on it and a list of courses to go on when she had time (which seemed to be never, these days).

Next she colour coded everything and changed the font style.

And size.

And colour.

And style.

And then she put it back to the way it was originally.

Next she decided it was time to take action.

To really take action, she would need to make a full assessment of the

Machine of Ultimate Prizes.

She measured it,

photographed it

assessed the weight ratio

length of lever

how many times it could be pulled in one hour

size of the penny slot

counted each and every prize

and finally read the label (one which she herself had designed in her previous job).

The label read:

'Analyzing the Machine of Ultimate Prizes is a Waste of Your Time. You Will Only Have a Chance to Win the Box of Dreams if You Take Action. For Health and Safety Reasons, We Recommend You Keep the Status Quo.'

Jenny went home and had a cup of tea.

She was no closer to winning even a small prize, but she did feel very learned and accomplished.

After all, she had been very busy, hadn't she?

It was then that Jenny realised how much she loved sticky labels.

She immediately labelled all her shiny pennies, which made her feel a lot better. Then she labelled her desk, chair, filing cabinet, window latch and coffee mug.

Jenny also loved pens.

After a very busy morning, EVERYTHING in Jenny's home office was covered in sticky labels, written in an array of colours and styles. There were sticky labels on the walls, the floors and ceilings, even on her shoes!

Eventually she sat down, exhausted.

And realised there was a slight problem.

She couldn't see the pennies any more.

And she had forgotten what the Box of Dreams looked like.

What Joe Did Next

Now Joe was an altogether different kettle of fish.

To start with, he liked to keep things simple.

It wasn't about throwing handfuls of coins randomly at the machine like Jack.

Nor was it about being busy but never taking action, like Jenny.

He knew that if he put a penny in the slot, he might win a prize.

And he might not.

The machine might make that rude belching sound and spit the coin right back out at him. That made him feel uncomfortable.

But if he didn't put a penny in, he definitely wouldn't win a prize.

So, he thought, if I put enough pennies in, carefully, one at a time without worrying about what happens next, I will probably at least get something. I don't mind if it's just a small prize. I just want to know I can win.

I need to do something differently from Jack and Jenny if I want to win the Box of Dreams.

Two Years Later

The way that Jack and Jenny first heard the news wasn't the way they expected.

It was Joe's birthday and he had called his old friends Jack and Jenny to come and celebrate with him. Just a few quiet drinks and a meal at the local Italian.

Tasty.

It was when they were munching happily through the oven-baked crust of the authentic Italian pizza base that Jenny noticed a small glittering corner poking out of Joe's top pocket.

She asked him what it was.

In a friendly, almost casual way, Joe took out the small gold box and placed it carefully on the table. Slowly he opened it up.

As he did so, a magical thing happened.

There was the Superman cape Joe had worn when he was five... the little plane he'd had when he dreamed of flying... a tiny model of a hospital he had said he'd love to build one day to take care of sick children.

They peered in wonder at the objects coming out of the box. And as they looked, they could see movements, hear sounds, and as they bent down to touch, they realised it was all real.

"Wow!" they breathed.

All the dreams Joe had ever had were shared around that table. And now he was creating even more beautiful and bigger dreams for the future.

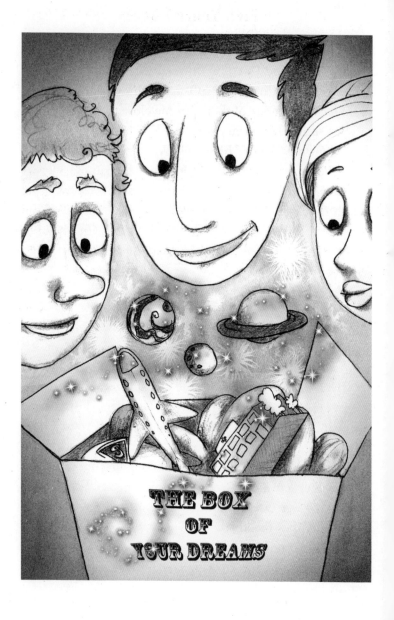

"That's the magic of this prize" said Joe. "You can choose. And you keep choosing."

"How on earth did you do it, Joe? I mean, you were a bus driver before and I went to university!" gasped Jenny.

"And I must have had SO many shiny pennies myself," said Jack, "but none of them got me close to this!"

Joe smiled his warm smile.

"Well, my friends," he said,

"The truth is, it may not be easy, but it is simple. I'll share the secret of how I did it so that you, and those who hear about this, if they choose can create their own success. I can't promise that you'll win the Box of Dreams… but I can tell you that it IS possible.

"For you.

"And for anyone who chooses wisely."

Joe's Secret

Like you, I had always been raised to accept that if I kept my head down, got a steady job and took care of the family, I was living a good life. That that was what I should expect and accept as my lot in life. That I was just an 'Average Joe'.

Like you, I had always relied on the Ringmaster to operate the machine for me and decide on the prize I was to receive each month (and it was always small and always exactly the same).

But then, just like you, there came a time for me when I knew I had to leave the old familiar ways and take a risk.

I started just like you did, with a small prize to help me get started, and beyond that no idea where the next prize would be coming from, now that I no longer had the Ringmaster to rely on.

I spent the small prize I had on someone to do the things that would have slowed me down—the admin, book-keeping and so on. It wasn't that I could afford it, it was that I needed to in order to have time to get out there and take action.

And it wasn't that I couldn't do these things myself, Jenny, it's more that if I spent all my time doing those jobs I'd never have had the time to choose a penny and put it into the Machine of Ultimate Prizes. So I wouldn't have won anything.

Like you, Jack, I found lots and lots of shiny pennies. It's funny isn't it? You start with just one or two, convinced that they will be the sure-fire way to win the Box of Dreams. Then, as you look about you, more and more shiny pennies appear!

I quickly realised that I needed a way to decide which of the pennies to use first, otherwise I'd have just ended up throwing them in great handfuls at the machine like you, Jack, and they'd have just bounced off.

So I created an idea so simple that ANYONE can do it, even an Average Joe like me, and turn it into a way of opening the Box of Dreams.

Joe took out his notebook and began to draw...

On the page he drew three columns.

At the top of the first he wrote, 'Shiny Pennies'.

"Every time I find a shiny penny," he said, "I write it down in my 'Shiny Pennies' column. Sometimes I find five or six in the same place, other times just one, and still other times there seem to be no new shiny pennies at all.

"But because I've written them all down, I know that when I need them, they'll be there, and when I don't need them, I can concentrate because I've made sure all the shiny pennies are safe.

"Next, I choose just ONE penny from my list of Shiny Pennies. It has to be the one I feel is most likely to earn a prize. A really special one.

"My second column is headed: 'Spend a Penny'.

"When I move my shiny penny over, I put a date underneath it, and then how long I will be happy to 'Spend a Penny'.

"Sometimes the penny gets returned with a large belch the first time, but on the second or third time a little prize pops out. Other times I get a prize right away, and other times I pop the shiny penny in lots of times and no prize pops out.

"Once I reach the penny's finish date, I take it off the 'Spend a Penny' list and either throw it away or put it back on my 'Shiny Penny' list for another day.

"Sometimes the shiny penny wins me a prize BEFORE its date. If that happens, I put it in my third column. My third column is the 'Earn A Penny' column. Once a shiny penny goes there, I can either keep doing what I'm doing to create more, or add another one from my 'Shiny Penny' list to my 'Spend a Penny' list.

"That way, only the good pennies can stay and I never end up being a 'Jack of all trades' and just throwing handfuls of coins aimlessly hoping for something to come back."

Jack and Jenny were quiet for quite a long time.

Eventually Jenny asked, "But how come the machine didn't just belch out all your shiny pennies?"

"It did," said Joe. "Many times."

"And what did you do?" asked Jack.

"I analysed what happened, accepted the learnings and carried on working through my shiny pennies. I knew that eventually some of them would come good. All I had to do was keep taking action and keep learning. I realised the machine wasn't being mean when it made the belching sound. It was just what it was programmed to do. And that's what eventually led me to the Ultimate Prize: The Box of Dreams."

"So HOW did you win the prize in the end?" asked Jack.

"Well," replied Joe, "that's another story..."

"I could never do that." said Jack.

"I think that if I follow your system Joe, I can do it one day," said Jenny.

Joe nodded slowly and said...

"That's right.

"Because whether you think you can, or whether you think you can't, you're right."

What to do Next

At times, it's easy for us entrepreneurs to become like Jack and Jenny.

We start out all fired up, full of ideas.

Perhaps we build a website, get a business advisor, check our numbers and push things forward.

Suddenly, up pops another idea. Just as shiny, just as compelling as the first one we had. We can get so carried away with following each new idea that we never complete or follow through anything.

We risk becoming either a 'Jack of all Trades' or a 'Juggling Jenny', caught up so much in the busy that we never fully take action to grow our business.

The truth is though, there's something that has driven you to go beyond the 'norm'. You've decided, for whatever reason, to step outside the PAYE comfort zone and go for it.

And why?

Because you want your dreams back.

Maybe it's time with the family, holidays, a secure lifestyle…. or perhaps it's even bigger than that and you have ideas and dreams to change the world.

Well done!

You've taken the road less travelled.

And you CAN do it.

What to do Next

Any 'Average Joe' can become extraordinary if they do it right.

This little book is designed to help you avoid a few of the most common pitfalls and to deal with one of the common reasons entrepreneurs fail: they don't know how to deal with all the shiny pennies!

By using the simple process outlined by Joe, and going through the exercise in your 'Shiny Penny System', you will have created a way of knowing which of your many shiny pennies to use.

The key is understanding which shiny pennies will lead you closer to the Ultimate Prize: The Box of Dreams, and which are a pretty distraction.

Using the Shiny Penny system, you can easily and quickly work out which ideas bring a return on your time and efforts and which are best let go of, at least until you have won a few more prizes.

Always remember your 'why': it's in the Box of Dreams.

So open it up...

...take a good look...

...and believe.

Enjoy Spending a Penny!

The Shiny Penny System™

How to do it

This is a really simple system, that can form a habit that you can do in just a few minutes.

Once it becomes something you do regularly (about once a week is great), you will notice your business becomes more focused, more productive and earns you money more quickly.

1. What is a Shiny Penny?

A shiny penny is an idea that comes to you and you think—WOW—I should really do that! It really is that simple.

When any idea comes to you, make a quick note—maybe in your phone, a notebook, whatever comes to hand. That way, you have immediately made a commitment to review it later, which allows you to release it from your mind and concentrate on what you need to do there and then, without getting distracted (distraction can be the downside of being highly creative and entrepreneurial). At this stage, just make a note—the idea can be absolutely anything and about anything. Just get it out of your mind and save it for later, allowing your mind some space for new ones.

2. What do I do next?

At the end of each week, have a time where you commit to counting your shiny pennies. All the ideas you have collected need to be subjected to the 'Shiny Penny' test.

If they pass the 'Shiny Penny' test, they make it onto the Shiny Penny board. If they don't, either leave them written down and remind yourself that you can return to them when you want to, or let them go and consider them complete in time. Trust that the first thing that comes to mind about them is usually the right response.

3. *The Shiny Penny Test*

To decide which ideas are 'Shiny Pennies', take the idea and ask it the following questions. Remember that for each question you are going to trust the very first thought that comes to you rather than spend ages pondering—there'll be plenty of time for rational processing later—just park that for now and go with the first thing that comes to mind for each of these 10 questions.

Remember—the way to do these questions is at high speed—the faster the better. One-word answers are fine.

a) What do I love about this idea?
b) Can I do it?
c) What do I want to achieve from it?
d) Can I achieve that?
e) Who is it for? (if it's a product or service it needs a target audience!)
f) Why will they love it?
g) Why won't they love it?
h) Who else would buy this?
i) Would I be happy for my granny, mother, trusted long-term friend, partner etc to buy this from someone?

j) How will I know when this idea has achieved success and completion?

k) Is it a lead balloon or will it fly? (really, really, REALLY trust the first thing that comes to mind on this one!)

4. Decision Time

Did it pass? Pay particular attention to b,d,i,k. These require only a quick yes/no by way of answer. it is ONLY a shiny penny if ALL these are clear positives! The other answers require a little more detail—but just keep it very quick and basic at this point. Remember—you are trusting the first thing that comes to mind. You'll fill in the detail later.

5. It's a Shiny Penny!

Positive answers immediately on all ten questions? Congratulations, you've found a shiny penny! Put it in your Shiny Penny column (the one on the left). That's just the beginning. Now go to 9.

6. It's a Lead Balloon!

Non-positive answers? Any at all? It won't fly, either because it's a lead balloon, or because you don't yet believe in the idea, or yourself, enough. Let it go (ONLY after checking 7). If you don't find this very easy, a good way to do this is to imagine the idea on the floor by your feet, with you looking down at it (looking can be visually, or you can create an internal representation of this through feeling or sound if that's easier for you). As you pay attention to it, it changes from solid, to liquid, to gas until it dissolves gently into nothing, leaving space for you to create something that will fly. Remember—the idea itself might be great, but if you don't believe in it or yourself sufficiently, it's either not right, or not the right time for you.

7. *What to do following a Lead Balloon.*

If it's the idea that is the problem, you'll discover that through your answers to e, f, g, h and your instinctive responses to those answers.

If it's your beliefs about yourself that are sabotaging the great ideas that come your way, then you might find lots of great ideas, yet you don't yet find it totally easy to give a congruent "yes" to b and d instinctively. If this is the case you have two options:

1) Quit like Jack
2) Do some work on yourself and then come back to the ideas when you've released the things that are holding you back—that way you'll discover a lot more shiny pennies, and what's more, you'll know what to do with them and have the self-belief to ensure they—and you—are consistently successful!

8. *Working on Yourself*

The most effective way to do this is either to undertake high-quality personal development training or to find a coach or mentor you can trust, have good rapport with and who knows their stuff. Most importantly, you are looking for someone that will deliver value, rather than a cheap price. Remember, if someone doesn't value what they do highly, how can they teach you to value yourself and what you want to achieve in business? There are plenty of coaches, hypno-therapists, Neuro Linguistic Programming (NLP) Business leaders etc...but whom do you trust? Well first of all you need to ensure they are credible. Anyone can be found at the top of an online search with the help of a good technical team, but being visible doesn't make someone good at what they do. Sites such as the ANLP, ABH and ABNLP are good tests of credibility: they list only those whose certificates are valid, recognised and whom they have personally checked. Someone with basic training will be at Practitioner Level, a higher level which allows work in more areas is Master Practitioner Level. Then there is Trainer level which is usually someone who works in their own private practice and also is qualified to certify Practitioners and Master Practitioners.

You might want to check out Breakthrough sessions (a Trainer or Master Practitioner from a credible training school will be able to offer these): a quick, powerful and content-free (no story-telling!) process to permanently release past negative emotions and limiting beliefs, especially empowering in the areas of business and relationships.

If you would like more information on personal development, Breakthrough Process, NLP, Hypnotherapy, Timeline Therapy™ or Coaching, or advice on how to find something that suits what you want to achieve, you are welcome to email admin@lifereturns.co.uk. As far as I am able, I answer every email personally, even if that may take a little while!

9. *Shiny Pennies...*
Now you have found your Shiny Pennies, it's time to get them onto your Shiny Penny board.

Column 1—Here you can write any idea that has made it to Shiny Penny status. I'd suggest no more than 10 on the list to start with (remember Jack…).

Put a star by your three favourites.

10. Spend a Penny

Pick the best one of the three. This is the exciting bit—you're going to spend a penny. Pop it on your 'Spend a Penny' board.

11. Set a Goal for your Penny

This is where you decide how much you will earn from this idea and by when. Make sure this is realistic for you. For tips on consistently setting and achieving goals effectively contact info@lifereturns.co.uk and we'll be glad to help. Write the date and time you will have achieved this. If the date and time are too far ahead into the future, you might need to make it into manageable stages with dates a bit closer, to ensure you are always working towards the next phase.

If the Penny is a big earner but won't give a return for a year, you might want to create something that you can sell more quickly even if it brings in a little less. This delicate balance of business is something I help in more detail with in the next book in this series, *Dinner Money*.

12. The Third column :Earn a Penny!

Here's where it gets exciting! If you've done the earlier steps right, you will know how much money your Shiny Penny is due to bring in and by what specific date and time (remember to include the year too!). If it's a little idea, the date will come around pretty fast; for a bigger idea you may be looking at a step in the process being completed. Whichever it is, set a reminder in your calendar (or write in your diary if you use a paper one) to remind you that it's 'Earn a Penny' day. Check on your Shiny Penny:

1) Has it earned the amount you said it would on time?

   If it has, and is still earning, you can either keep doing it, or put it aside as you wish… AND you get to move another idea from your Shiny Penny column to your 'Spend a Penny" one. And off you go again!

   If not:

2) Has it earned anything? Is it likely to in the near future?

   If it has earned something, have a look at whether this is likely to increase, as well as whether the amount has been worth the time and effort put in (remember the importance of trusting the first answer that comes to mind). If you have a congruent 'Yes', then continue with the idea, perhaps introducing one of your smaller Shiny Pennies to run alongside it—just one!

3) Has it earned nothing at all?

   It's time to cross the idea off your Shiny Penny board and move on.

   Remember—if it's become a lead balloon—let it go!

   Pick your next Shiny Penny and go for it!

And finally...

The key thing to remember with this system is that it is only one learning you can receive from this book. There may be other learnings you gain by simply enjoying the story. Remember that the most effective people are those who continually develop themselves, which causes their business to grow alongside them (see 8). Clients are attracted as much by who you are as by what you can offer them and the more you work on yourself, the more you have to offer.

If you stick to the Shiny Penny System precisely, it will work. If you remember to cross off one shiny penny before spending the next, it will work.

If you throw Shiny Pennies all over it, you will get tired, the pennies will lose their shine and you'll not reach that place where the pennies begin to turn into hundreds, then thousands then millions...

And remember that the amount you earn isn't about cash in the bank, it's about what you are enabled to do....

for you...

for those you care about...

and to make a positive difference in this world.

Remember the wise words of Gandhi:

'Be the change you want to see in the world.'

And you will.

The Author

'If it's life-giving—embrace it, if it's life denying, let it go.'
Rose Cleaver-Emons

The Shiny Penny™ System

Spend a Penny

"What is the BIG IDEA then?"

_____

_____

Date & time of completion:

DAY _____ MONTH _____ YEAR _____

Time _____

Amount Earned: £/$ _____ (Net/Gross)

_____

Do I need to break it into stages?

Yes/No

Earn a Penny

How much did I earn?

£/$ _____

When?

(Date:) _____

(Time:) _____

1) Date: _____

   Time: _____

   Amount: £/$ _____

2) Date: _____

   Time: _____

   Amount: £/$ _____

Shiny Penny

1

2

3

4

5

Stage 1

Date: _____

Time: _____

Amount: £/$ _____ (Net/Grass)

Stage 2

Date: _____

Time: _____

Amount: £/$ _____ (Net/Grass)

Stage 3

Date: _____

Time: _____

Amount: £/$ _____ (Net/Grass)

3) Date: _____

Time: _____

Amount: £/$ _____

TOTAL: _____

How much did I spend?

Time: _____

Resources: _____

Did I make a profit? _____

How much? _____

Next Action? _____

_____

The Shiny Penny(TM) System

Spend a Penny

"What is the BIG IDEA then?"

_____

_____

Date & time of completion:

DAY _____ MONTH _____ YEAR _____

Time _____

Amount Earned: _£/$_ _____ (Net/Gross)

_____

Do I need to break it into stages?

Yes/No

Earn a Penny

How much did I earn?

_£/$_ _____

When?

(Date:) _____

(Time:) _____

1) Date: _____

   Time: _____

   Amount: _£/$_ _____

2) Date: _____

   Time: _____

   Amount: _£/$_ _____

Shiny Penny

1

2

3

4

5

Stage 1

Date: _____

Time: _____

Amount: £/$ _____ (Net/Grass)

Stage 2

Date: _____

Time: _____

Amount: £/$ _____ (Net/Grass)

Stage 3

Date: _____

Time: _____

Amount: £/$ _____ (Net/Grass)

3) Date: _____

Time: _____

Amount: £/$ _____

TOTAL: _____

How much did I spend?

Time: _____

Resources: _____

Did I make a profit? _____

How much? _____

Next Action? _____

_____

The Shiny Penny(TM) System

Spend a Penny

"What is the BIG IDEA then?"

_____

_____

Date & time of completion:

DAY _____ MONTH _____ YEAR _____

Time _____

Amount Earned: £/$ _____ (Net/Gross)

_____

Do I need to break it into stages?

Yes/No

Earn a Penny

How much did I earn?

£/$ _____

When?

(Date:) _____

(Time:) _____

1) Date: _____

   Time: _____

   Amount: £/$ _____

2) Date: _____

   Time: _____

   Amount: £/$ _____

Shiny Penny

1

2

3

4

5

Stage 1

Date: _____

Time: _____

Amount: £/$ _____ (Net/Grass)

Stage 2

Date: _____

Time: _____

Amount: £/$ _____ (Net/Grass)

Stage 3

Date: _____

Time: _____

Amount: £/$ _____ (Net/Grass)

3) Date: _____

Time: _____

Amount: £/$ _____

TOTAL: _____

How much did I spend?

Time: _____

Resources: _____

Did I make a profit? _____

How much? _____

Next Action? _____

The Shiny Penny™ System

Spend a Penny

"What is the BIG IDEA then?"

_____

_____

Date & time of completion:

DAY _____ MONTH _____ YEAR _____

Time _____

Amount Earned: £/$ _____ (Net/Gross)

_____

Do I need to break it into stages?

Yes/No

Earn a Penny

How much did I earn?

£/$

_____

When?

(Date:) _____

(Time:) _____

1) Date: _____

   Time: _____

   Amount: £/$ _____

2) Date: _____

   Time: _____

   Amount: £/$ _____

Shiny Penny

1

2

3

4

5

Stage 1

Date: _____

Time: _____

Amount: £/$ _____ (Net/Grass)

3) Date: _____

    Time: _____

    Amount: £/$ _____

TOTAL: _____

Stage 2

Date: _____

Time: _____

Amount: £/$ _____ (Net/Grass)

How much did I spend? _____

Time: _____

Resources: _____

Stage 3

Date: _____

Time: _____

Amount: £/$ _____ (Net/Grass)

Did I make a profit? _____

How much? _____

Next Action? _____

6

7

8

9

10

The Shiny Penny(TM) System

Spend a Penny

"What is the BIG IDEA then?"

_____

_____

Date & time of completion:

DAY _____ MONTH _____ YEAR _____

Time _____

Amount Earned: _£/$_ _____ (Net/Gross)

_____

Do I need to break it into stages?

Yes/No

Earn a Penny

How much did I earn?

_£/$_ _____

When?

(Date:) _____

(Time:) _____

1) Date: _____

   Time: _____

   Amount: _£/$_

2) Date: _____

   Time: _____

   Amount: _£/$_

Shiny Penny

1

2

3

4

5

Stage 1

Date: _____

Time: _____

Amount: £/$ _____ (Net/Grass)

Stage 2

Date: _____

Time: _____

Amount: £/$ _____ (Net/Grass)

Stage 3

Date: _____

Time: _____

Amount: £/$ _____ (Net/Grass)

3) Date: _____

Time: _____

Amount: £/$ _____

TOTAL: _____

How much did I spend? _____

Time: _____

Resources: _____

Did I make a profit? _____

How much? _____

Next Action? _____

_____

6 _____

7 _____

8 _____

9 _____

10 _____

The Shiny Penny(TM) System

Shiny Penny

1

2

3

4

5

Spend a Penny

"What is the BIG IDEA then?"

_____

_____

Date & time of completion:

DAY _____ MONTH _____ YEAR _____

Time _____

Amount Earned: £/$ _____ (Net/Gross)

_____

Do I need to break it into stages?

Yes/No

Earn a Penny

How much did I earn?

£/$ _____

When?

(Date:) _____

(Time:) _____

1) Date: _____

Time: _____

Amount: _____ £/$

2) Date: _____

Time: _____

Amount: _____ £/$

Stage 1

Date: _____

Time: _____

Amount: £/$ _____ (Net/Grass)

Stage 2

Date: _____

Time: _____

Amount: £/$ _____ (Net/Grass)

Stage 3

Date: _____

Time: _____

Amount: £/$ _____ (Net/Grass)

3) Date: _____

Time: _____

Amount: £/$ _____

TOTAL: _____

How much did I spend? _____

Time: _____

Resources: _____

Did I make a profit? _____

How much? _____

Next Action? _____

_____

6

7

8

9

10

The Shiny Penny(TM) System

Shiny Penny

1

2

3

4

5

Spend a Penny

"What is the BIG IDEA then?"

_____

_____

Date & time of completion:

DAY _____ MONTH _____ YEAR _____

Time _____

Amount Earned: £/$ _____ (Net/Gross)

_____

Do I need to break it into stages?

Yes/No

Earn a Penny

How much did I earn?

£/$ _____

When?

(Date:) _____

(Time:) _____

1) Date: _____

   Time: _____

   Amount: £/$ _____

2) Date: _____

   Time: _____

   Amount: £/$ _____

Stage 1

Date: _____

Time: _____

Amount: £/$ _____ _____ (Net/Grass)

Stage 2

Date: _____

Time: _____

Amount: £/$ _____ _____ (Net/Grass)

Stage 3

Date: _____

Time: _____

Amount: £/$ _____ _____ (Net/Grass)

3) Date: _____

Time: _____

Amount: £/$ _____

TOTAL: _____

How much did I spend? _____

Time: _____

Resources: _____

Did I make a profit? _____

How much? _____

Next Action? _____
_____

The Shiny Penny(TM) System

Spend a Penny

"What is the BIG IDEA then?"

_____

_____

Date & time of completion:

DAY _____ MONTH _____ YEAR _____

Time _____

Amount Earned: £/$ _____ (Net/Gross)

_____

Do I need to break it into stages?

Yes/No

Earn a Penny

How much did I earn?

£/$ _____

When?

(Date:) _____

(Time:) _____

1) Date: _____

    Time: _____

    Amount: £/$ _____

2) Date: _____

    Time: _____

    Amount: _____ £/$

Shiny Penny

1

2

3

4

5

Stage 1

Date: _____

Time: _____

Amount: £/$ _____ (Net/Grass)

Stage 2

Date: _____

Time: _____

Amount: £/$ _____ (Net/Grass)

Stage 3

Date: _____

Time: _____

Amount: £/$ _____ (Net/Grass)

3) Date: _____

Time: _____

Amount: £/$ _____

TOTAL: _____

How much did I spend? _____

Time: _____

Resources: _____

Did I make a profit? _____

How much? _____

Next Action? _____

_____